Rhymes for Bedtime

FOR
PARENTS OF SLEEPLESS CHILDREN EVERYWHERE

A Red Fox Book

Published by Random House Children's Books
20 Vauxhall Bridge Road, London SW1V 2SA

A division of Random House UK Ltd
London Melbourne Sydney Auckland
Johannesburg and agencies throughout the world

Compilation and illustrations © Sarah Pooley 1991

3 5 7 9 10 8 6 4

First published in Great Britain by The Bodley Head 1991

Red Fox edition 1994

Printed in China

RANDOM HOUSE UK Limited Reg. No. 954009

ISBN 0 09 987460 1

185656 4029

Rhymes for Bedtime

Selected and Illustrated by

SARAH POOLEY

RED FOX

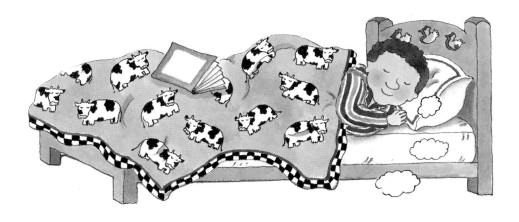

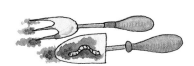

my favourite
Animal by Slow

To bed, to bed
Says Sleepy Head
Tarry awhile says Slow
Put on the pan
Says Greedy Nan
we'll sup before we go.

My favourit food
by Greedy Nan

my favourite place
by Sleepy
Head

more
milk!

mustard
seeds

As I was going up the stair
I met a man who wasn't there
He wasn't there again today
How I wish he'd go away!

Up the wooden hill to Blanket Fair
What shall we have when we get there?
A bucket full of water and penny worth of hay . . .

Rub-a-dub-dub
Three men in a tub
And who do you think they be?
The butcher, the baker
The candlestick maker,
Turn them out, knaves all three.

Here is the sea, the wavy sea
Here is the boat and here is me
All the little fishes down below
Wriggle their tails, and away they all go .

This little pig had a rub-a-dub
This little pig had a scrub-a-scrub
This little pig-a-wig ran upstairs
This little pig-a-wig called out, Bears!
Down came the jar with a loud Slam! Slam!
This little pig had all the jam .

Bears!

Strawberry
Jam

for Pig-a-wigs

Little man in coalpit goes
Knock, Knock, Knock,
Up he comes, up he comes
out the top!

Comb my hair said Lady Fair
And put some grease upon it
Not too much of the nasty stuff
Or you'll spoil my nice new bonnet.

It's raining, it's pouring
The little old man is snoring
He went to bed with a bump on
his head
And didn't get up in the
morning.

Weary Willie, and tired Tim
Went to bed, but they couldn't get in
So they sat on the ground
And had a look around –
Weary Willie and Tired Tim.

In winter I get up at night
And dress by yellow candle light
In summer quite the other way
I have to go to bed by day

I have to go to bed and see
The birds still hopping on the tree
Or hear the grown-up people's feet
Still going past me in the street

And does it not seem hard to you
When all the sky is clear and blue
And I should like so much to play
To have to go to bed by day?

ROBERT LOUIS STEVENSON

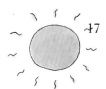

Go to bed first
a golden purse
Go to bed second
a golden pheasant
Go to bed third
a golden bird!

When all the cows were sleeping
And the sun had gone to bed
Up jumped the scarecrow
And this is what he said
I'm a dingle, dangle scarecrow
With a flippy, floppy hat
I can shake my hands like this
and shake my feet like that
When all the hens were roosting
And the moon behind the cloud
Up jumped the scarecrow
And shouted very loud . . .

M. RUSSELL SMITH &
G. RUSSELL SMITH .

I'm a dingle dangle scarecrow ... etc.

Wee Willie Winkie runs through the town
Upstairs and downstairs in his nightgown
Rapping at the window, crying through the lock
Are the children all in bed, for now it's eight o'clock.

Boys and girls come out to play
The moon doth shine as bright as day
Leave your supper and leave your sleep
And join your playfellows in the street!
Come with a whoop and come with a call,
Come with a good will or not at all.
Up the ladder and down the wall
A half penny loaf will serve us all
You find milk and I'll find flour
And we'll have a pudding in half an hour.

Trot, trot, trot,
Go and never stop
Trudge along, my little pony,
Where'tis rough and where'tis stony,
go and never stop
Trot, trot, trot, trot, trot!

Here is the ostrich straight and tall
Nodding his head above us all
Here is the long snake on the ground
Wriggling upon the stones he found
Here are the birds that fly so high
Spreading their wings across the sky.

tweet! tweet!

Here is the hedgehog prickly small
Rolling himself into a ball
Here is the spider scuttling around
Treading so lightly on the ground
Here are the children fast asleep
And here at nightfall owls do peep.

BOYCE AND BARTLETT

snore!

twit-twoo!

Are you ticklish Teddy?

Round, and round the garden
Like a teddy bear
One step, two step
Tickle you under there!

There was an old owl who lived in an oak
The more he heard the less he spoke
The less he spoke, the more he heard
Why aren't we like that wise old bird?

Hey diddle, diddle
The cat and the fiddle
The cow jumped over the moon
The little dog laughed to see such a sight
And the dish ran away with the spoon.

Dance to your daddy
My little babby
Dance to you daddy
My little lamb

You shall have a fishy
In a little dishy
You shall have a fishy
When the boat comes in

You shall have an apple
You shall have a plum
You shall have a rattle
When your daddy comes home.

One fine October morning
In September last July
The moon lay thick upon the ground
The snow shone in the sky
The flowers were singing gaily
And the birds were in full bloom
I went down to the cellar
To sweep the upstairs room

With my little broom, I sweep sweep sweep
On my little toes I creep creep creep
With my little eyes I peep peep peep
On my little bed I sleep sleep sleep.

ELIZABETH BARNARD

Hey-how for Halloween
All the witches to be seen
Some black and some green
Hey-how for Halloween .

The Man in the Moon as he sails the sky
Is a very remarkable skipper
But he made a mistake when he tried to take
A drink of milk for the Dipper
He dipped it into the Milky Way
And slowly and carefully filled it
The Big Bear growled and the Little Bear howled
And scared him so that he spilled it!

There was an old woman
who made green cheese
By beating up spinach
and curds with a spoon
And when she had done it
with very great ease
Tossed it up to the sky
and declared'twas the moon.

To sleep easy all night
Let your supper be light
Or else you'll complain
Of a stomach in pain.

O Timothy Tim
Has ten pink toes
And ten pink toes
Has Timothy Tim
They go with him
Wherever he goes
And wherever he goes
They go with him

O Timothy Tim
Has two blue eyes
And two blue eyes
Has Timothy Tim
They cry with him
Whenever he cries
And whenever he cries
They cry with him

O Timothy Tim
Has one red head
And one red head
Has Timothy Tim
It sleeps with him
In Timothy's bed
Sleep well red head
Of Timothy Tim.

A. A. MILNE

Rock-a-bye baby on the tree top
When the wind blows the cradle will rock
When the bough breaks the cradle will fall
Down will come baby, cradle and all .

Sleep baby sleep
The father watches the sheep
The mother is shaking the dreamland tree
And softly a little dream falls on thee
Sleep, baby, sleep.

Golden slumbers
Kiss your eyes
Smiles await you
When you rise
Sleep little baby
Don't you cry
And I will sing a lullaby.

El Coqui sings a sweet song at twilight
He is singing as sleep comes to me
When I wake all alone in the moonlight
El Coqui sings goodnight from the tree
Co-qui, Co-qui, Co-qui, qui, qui, qui .

Here are the lady's knives and forks
Here is the lady's table
Here is the lady's looking glass
And here is the baby's cradle .

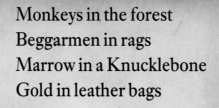

Monkeys in the forest
Beggarmen in rags
Marrow in a Knucklebone
Gold in leather bags

Dumplings in the oven
Fishes in a pool
Flowers in a parlour
Dunces in a school

Feathers in a pillow
Cattle in a shed
Honey in a beehive
And me in bed.

WALTER DE LA MARE

Softly, softly falling snow
This is how the snowflakes go
Pitter, patter, pitter, patter
Pit pit pat
Down go the raindrops
On my hat .

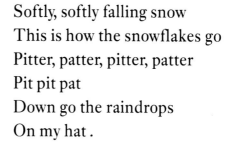

Silent night, ho-ly night
All is calm, all is bright
Round yon vir-gin mother and child
Ho-ly infant so ten-der and mild
Sleep in hea-ven-ly peace
Sleep in hea-ven-ly peace .

Nativity scene here today with carol concert. starts at 7 o'clock

Advent Calendar

Away in a manger, no crib for a bed
The little Lord Jesus laid down his sweet head
The stars in the bright sky
Looked down where he lay
The Little Lord Jesus asleep on the hay.

Christmas Carols for children

Little Jesus, sweetly sleep, do not stir
We will send you a coat of fur
We will rock you, rock you, rock you
We will rock you, rock you, rock you
See the fur to keep you warm
Snugly round your tiny form.

Star light, star bright
First star I've seen tonight
Wish I may wish I might
Have this wish I wish tonight.

Jellicle cats come out tonight
Jellicle cats come one and all
The Jellicle Moon is shining bright
Jellicles come to the Jellicle Ball

Jellicle cats are black and white
Jellicle cats are rather small
Jellicle cats are merry and bright
And pleasant to hear when they caterwaul
Jellicle cats have cheerful faces
Jellicle cats have bright black eyes
They like to practice their airs and graces
And wait for the Jellicle Moon to rise . . .

T. S. ELIOT

One, two, three, four o'clock, four o'clock rock
Five, six, seven o'clock, eight o'clock rock
Nine, ten, eleven o'clock, twelve o'clock rock
We're gonna rock, gonna rock around the clock tonight
Rock around the clock tonight
We're gonna rock, rock rock till broad daylight
We're gonna rock, gonna rock around the clock tonight!

MAX FREEDMAN & JIMMY DE KNIGHT

The clock
Ticks
The clock
Tocks
This way,
That way,
And never never
Stops
Tick-tock
Tick-tock
Tick-tock.

As soon as I'm in bed at night
And snugly settled down
The little girl I am by day
Goes very suddenly away
And then I'm Mrs Brown

I have a family of six
And all of them have names
The girls are Joyce and Nancy Maud
The boys are Marmaduke and Claude
And Percival and James

We have a house with twenty rooms
A mile away from town
I think it's good for girls and boys
To be allowed to make a noise
And so does Mr Brown

We do the most exciting things
Enough to make you creep
And on and on and on we go
I sometimes wonder if I know
When I have gone to sleep.

ROSE FYLEMAN

Au clair de le Lu-ne, Mon a-mi Pier-rot,
Prê-te moi ta plu-me. Pour e-crire un mot.
Ma chan-delle est mor-te, Je n-ai plus defeu;
Ou-vre moi ta por-te, Pour l'amour de Dieu.

If I were a bear,
And a big bear too,
I shouldn't much care,
If it froze or snew;
I shouldn't much mind
If it snowed or friz —
I'd be all fur lined
With a coat like his

For I'd have fur boots and a brown fur wrap
And brown fur knickers and a big fur cap
I'd have a fur muffle-ruff to cover my jaws
And brown fur mittens on my big brown paws
With a big brown furry-down up to my head
I'd sleep all the winter in a big fur bed.

A. A. MILNE

From Breakfast on through all the day
At home among my friends I stay
But every night I go abroad
Afar into the Land of Nod

All by myself I have to go,
With none to tell me what to do —
All alone beside the streams
And up the mountainsides of dreams

The strangest things are there for me
Both things to eat and things to see
And many frightening sights abroad
Till morning in the Land of Nod

Try as I like to find the way
I never can get back by day
Nor can remember plain and clear
The curious music that I hear.

ROBERT LOUIS STEVENSON

INDEX OF FIRST LINES

ACKNOWLEDGEMENTS

The editor and publishers would like to thank the following for permission to use copyright material in this collection. The publishers have made every effort to contact the copyright holders but there have been a few cases where it has not been possible to do so. We would be grateful to hear from anyone who can enable us to contact them so that the omission can be corrected at the first opportunity.

Mrs Brown: courtesy of The Society of Authors as the literary representative of the Estate of Rose Fyleman

Monkeys in the Forest: courtesy of The Literary Trustees of Walter de la Mare, and The Society of Authors as their representative

Here is the ostrich straight and tall: Boyce and Bartlett from NURSERY RHYMES AND FINGER PLAYS ed. Elizabeth Matterson, Isaac Pitman & Sons Ltd

With my little broom I sweep, sweep, sweep: Elizabeth Barnard from NEW NURSERY JINGLES ed. Elizabeth Matterson, J. Curwin & Sons

Rock Around the Clock: written by Max Freedman & Jimmy de Knight © 1953 Myers Music Inc. for the World, used by kind permission of the Edward Kassner Music Co. Limited (UK representative)

The Jellicle Cats: from OLD POSSUMS BOOK OF PRACTICAL CATS by T. S. Eliot by kind permission of Faber & Faber Ltd and the estate of T. S. Eliot

Cradle Song and *Furry Bear*: A. A. Milne, Methuen Children's Books and Dutton Children's Books

When all the cows were sleeping by M. Russell Smith and G. Russell Smith © for the World Mills Music Limited, England © assigned 1987 CPP/Belwin Inc. USA. Reprinted by permission of CPP/Belwin Europe, Surrey, England

Some bestselling Red Fox picture books

THE BIG ALFIE AND ANNIE ROSE STORYBOOK
by Shirley Hughes
OLD BEAR
by Jane Hissey
OI! GET OFF OUR TRAIN
by John Burningham
DON'T DO THAT!
by Tony Ross
NOT NOW, BERNARD
by David McKee
ALL JOIN IN
by Quentin Blake
THE WHALES' SONG
by Gary Blythe and Dyan Sheldon
JESUS' CHRISTMAS PARTY
by Nicholas Allan
THE PATCHWORK CAT
by Nicola Bayley and William Mayne
WILLY AND HUGH
by Anthony Browne
THE WINTER HEDGEHOG
by Ann and Reg Cartwright
A DARK, DARK TALE
by Ruth Brown
HARRY, THE DIRTY DOG
by Gene Zion and Margaret Bloy Graham
DR XARGLE'S BOOK OF EARTHLETS
by Jeanne Willis and Tony Ross
WHERE'S THE BABY?
by Pat Hutchins